hair
affair

Wendy Lewis

hair affair

the lowdown on getting gorgeous hair

QUADRILLE

Editorial Director: Jane O'Shea

Creative Director: Mary Evans

Designer: Sue Storey

Project Editor: Lisa Pendreigh

Editor: Katie Ginn

Picture Research: Nadine Bazar

Illustrations: Sue Storey

Production: Nancy Roberts

First published in 2002 by Quadrille Publishing Limited
Alhambra House
27–31 Charing Cross Road
London WC2H OLS

Cataloguing-in-Publication Data: a catalogue record for this book is available from the British
Library.

ISBN 1 903845 69 6

Printed and bound in Singapore

Contents

Nothing beats a full head of glossy hair. It's one of the first things people notice and remember about you. The way a woman feels about her hair and the way she cares for it changes with the seasons as well as the stages and phases of her life. We are always keen to learn the secret of maintaining healthy hair, how to hang on to every last hair we have and how to manage it better and more beautifully. Now for the price of a latte, girls can get the real scoop on insider tips to a gorgeous mane.

This comprehensive guide delivers a fresh and modern approach to the beauty challenges we face in keeping hair thick, handling frizz or oiliness, colouring and straightening or just keeping up with the latest styles. It gives the lowdown on the most state-of-the-art methods, what works and what's a waste of money, top clinical advances, new para-surgical treatments, DIY home remedies, as well as resources for how to find a good doctor, shopping guides and web links.

GROOMING IT

GROOMING IT

Never underestimate the power of great hair. It is the frame around your face, the finishing touch to your total look. It is an essential part of your image and a great accessory. It's one of the first things you notice about a person.

A good hairstyle can be the ultimate fashion statement. Hairstyles change with the catwalks every season. But whatever the look, the operative word is thick. Both women and men tend to be most attracted to a head of hair that is dense, long and a good colour. The goal is shine, softness, strength and 'stylability', which are key indicators of healthy hair and what every woman craves.

The expression 'Bad Hair Day' has become a part of the vernacular. Its closest translation: If you're hair doesn't look good, you don't look good. Thin, limp or stringy hair makes you feel like a 'plain jane'. How you wear your hair says a lot about you. Gorgeous hair connotes real beauty and a new hairstyle is the quickest path to reinventing yourself. Faking it can be the next best thing.

clean regime

Just like your face, your hair needs a cleansing ritual for the morning, the evening and emergencies. These may change with the seasons.

Great-looking hair starts in the shower. Go gently on your follicles to maintain each strand for as long as you can and to keep them bouncy. Over-cleansing, pulling and tugging and too much styling and fixing can weaken hair and make it brittle. Many shampoo bottles have directions that instruct you to shampoo and rinse twice. The idea is that the first removes dirt, oil and product build-up and the second helps add volume, as well as providing a backup in case the first shampoo didn't get your hair clean enough. However, for dry or brittle hair, one shampoo may be enough.

The presence of airborne pollutants and holes in the ozone layer, and the use of steam heat, hot rollers and blow-dryers means your hair tends to attract dust and dirt. For some women, daily washing with a shampoo formulated to restore balance to hair and scalp is a necessity. Others are happy to skip a day or two. For short hair, daily washing is usually needed. Every other day for longer hair may be suitable, especially since the time involved to dry and style can be more than you can manage. Washing hair more than once a day is not necessary or recommended. The natural oils your hair produces each day provide thickness and shine that you don't want to strip away by over-washing.

shampoo selection

Selecting the right products for your hair type and condition will help you make the most of it. Start with the basics and add as needed. Your hair may grow tired of a product before you do.

Shampoos for coloured, permed or processed hair – Chemically processed hair needs special formulas that won't strip colour and contain ingredients that are gentle and moisturizing.

Highlighting or colour-enhancing shampoos – Designed to prevent colour from fading, they add tone and extend the life of your highlights. They add shine to grey hair and help reduce yellow. They are also good to use after a perm as the peroxide in neutralizers can lighten the colour of your hair.

Clarifying shampoos – These contain an acidic ingredient, such as apple cider, lemon juice or vinegar, to cut through residue built up by styling products. Use these before you colour, perm or relax your hair to allow the treatment to be absorbed better and go on more evenly. They are too drying to use every day, once or twice a week is enough. Overuse can cause excess stripping of the natural oils.

Volumizing or body-building shampoo – These contain proteins that bond to the hair to add volume. Use them sparingly as overuse may build up residue. For fine hair, alternate with a regular shampoo. Look for ingredients like 'dimethicone copolyol'; a silicon derivative that helps to build volume in hair.

5 step cleansing routine

The best shampoos should be at a pH of 4.5 to 6, which is the closest to the natural pH of the scalp and hair. Look for a pH balanced formula as some shampoos may be too harsh.

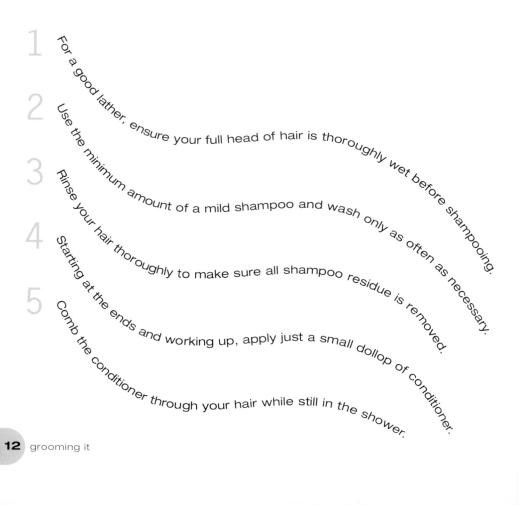

1 For a good lather, ensure your full head of hair is thoroughly wet before shampooing.

2 Use the minimum amount of a mild shampoo and wash only as often as necessary.

3 Rinse your hair thoroughly to make sure all shampoo residue is removed.

4 Starting at the ends and working up, apply just a small dollop of conditioner.

5 Comb the conditioner through your hair while still in the shower.

conditioner choices

Conditioners make the hair smoother and add body and shine, but there is a fine line between the right amount of conditioner and too much.

Conditioners are usually made of large molecules that literally stick to the outside of the hair and make combing easier, which prevents the hair from twisting and breaking. Hair tangles when the cuticle doesn't lie flat and the hairs can't slide past one another with ease. Because they coat the hair, conditioners make it look shiny and protect it from damage from the environment and styling tools. They usually contain silicone and moisture-producing substances like ceramides and complex lipids that smooth over hair and can reduce frizz and static electricity.

Although conditioners can add thickness and volume to thin and thinning hair, over-conditioning may cause hair to look greasy. It can cause the cuticle layer of the hair to lift, making it brittle. Whether you use conditioner or not depends on your hair. For thin hair, use only lightweight, rinse-out conditioners or cream rinses. Volumizers with ingredients like keratin, collagen and hydrolyzed proteins help to plump up strands for fuller-looking hair. Chemically processed hair needs conditioner to counteract the drying and damaging effects of the dyes and peroxides.

TOP TIP:
Conditioners should be at a low pH of 4.0 to 4.5 to maintain the protein in the hair.

Daily conditioners

Rinse-out conditioners
Most hair types

These reduce tangles, increase shine, smooth the hair cuticle, soften the hair and reduce static. They are used after shampooing and should be rinsed out thoroughly.

Leave-in conditioners
Dry hair

Frequently blow-dried hair will benefit from a leave-in conditioner. These treatments are usually applied to towel-dried hair. They coat the hair, making it heavier and weighing it down. Some formulas have UV protection built in to protect hair from sun, wind and heat.

Deep conditioners
Dry and damaged hair

These are suited to dry, chemically processed, damaged and weak hair that is in need of some TLC. They restore moisture and fortify strands of hair with proteins and moisturizing ingredients to repair split ends and brittleness. Treatments are usually left on for 10–30 minutes and rinsed out thoroughly.

All-in-one shampoos and conditioners
Most hair types

They may seem practical and economical, but shampoo/conditioner combos tend to leave a residue that builds up quickly and weighs hair down. They should never be used on oily hair. Best reserved for travel.

good condition

Most of us don't give conditioners time to work. Wait at least 5 minutes. Don't rinse out too soon before the conditioner has had chance to seep into the hair.

Thickening serums – *Fine hair* – Proteins and polymers are bound to the hair shaft, making hair appear fuller. Thickening serums can be applied to wet or dry hair before styling.

TOP TIP:

If your conditioner is too thick for your hair, dilute with warm water and shake vigorously to mix up before use.

Detanglers – *Fine and curly hair* – This works well as a substitute for conditioner on both fine and curly hair. Choose a light formula and rinse out thoroughly before combing hair.

Hot oils – *Dry or processed hair* – Adding oil is good for dry or processed hair. Massage a few drops directly into the scalp every 2–4 weeks. Apply lightly to avoid overgreasing.

the white stuff

The condition of your scalp can provide a useful clue to the health of your hair. A healthy scalp provides a strong foundation for a gorgeous, shiny head of hair.

Part your hair in a place near the crown where you can see it in the mirror. Run a fine-tooth comb gently across the scalp. See how much flaking you pick up. Some occasional flaking is normal and doesn't necessarily mean you have dandruff. It could be a form of dermatitis or eczema. Dandruff is characterized by a dry, itchy scalp and white flakes that show up on your shoulders, especially when you're wearing dark colours. Dandruff is a normal shedding of skin, and is actually a form of seborrhea that is more common in men than in women. The exact cause is unknown but contributing factors can include stress, sweating and hormones.

Dandruff can be present in dry or oily scalps, but is more common in oily skin types. The key to controlling dandruff is to remove the flakes as soon as they appear by frequent washing with a medicated shampoo which not only removes the dandruff but also cuts down on the rate of shedding. For most sufferers, dandruff is a lifetime condition that can be controlled by using the right shampoo.

TOP TIP:
African and black women tend to have drier hair, which is likely to attract flakes. Daily shampooing may not be necessary. Massage the scalp to stimulate your natural oils. A light textured oil can be used on the scalp, or ask your doctor about using a shampoo that contains a steroid.

Anti-dandruff shampoos

Over-the-counter medicated shampoos usually contain coal tar, salicylic acid (beta hydroxy acid), selenium sulphide or zinc pyrithione. Prescription strength sulphur, ketoconazole and topical steroids may also be used. If your hair is processed, avoid products with selenium sulphide or sulphur.

Severe forms of dandruff, where flakes are oilier and more yellowish than usual and the scalp is red and inflamed, might be Seborrheic Dermatitis, which requires treatment from a doctor. Use every day until your dandruff disappears. For maintenance, only use medicated shampoos as needed to avoid drying out your hair. Use a shampoo and conditioner for dry hair the rest of the time.

- **DON'T** use heavy conditioners and styling products designed to coat the hair as they can prevent the natural shedding of the scalp. This may cause a build-up of flakes.

- **DO** switch to a gentler product, which may reduce flaking if your scalp is reacting to a harsh ingredient in your shampoo.

- **DO** use a clarifying shampoo that contains cider, which may reduce product build-up and help to clear the scalp of flakes.

- **DO** use tea tree oil, which can be helpful as an antiseptic.

- **DO** give yourself regular scalp massages.

- **DO** try to avoid centrally heated rooms as dry scalp conditions can be aggravated by a lack of moisture in the air.

oil control

Hair has natural oils secreted from the sebaceous glands to protect hair and keep it shiny. Oily hair may be greasy at the scalp, but dull and dry at the ends.

Fine, thin hair is the most prone to looking oily and limp. Wash hair daily with a mild shampoo that does not contain a conditioner so it leaves the least amount of residue. Formulas specifically for oily hair and clarifying shampoos work well. Use only a very light creme rinse or a diluted formula on the ends only and rinse out thoroughly.

Greasy hair needs conditioning too, it just needs less. Avoid products containing silicone, mineral oils and lanolin which coat the hair, weigh it down and make the strands lie flat against the scalp. If your hair has become stringy by midday, spritz water on it and comb through to remove and redistribute oils. The goal is not to strip away all its natural oils.

In humid weather, you may shower and wash your hair more often, especially if oily. Switch to a gentle shampoo for frequent use. If you sweat a lot when exercising, shampoo after your workout.

It is time to switch shampoos if:

- you like your hair better the morning after you've washed it.
- your hair feels weighed down and you feel the need to rinse it more.
- your hair is hard to detangle or style.
- your hair doesn't look shiny.
- sudsing no longer gives you a rich lather.

Oil overdrive

Excess oil means your sebaceous glands are in overdrive. The waxy oil these glands produce not only gives hair a greasy appearance but also builds up on the scalp. When sebum hardens, it blocks blood flow and starves the roots embedded in the scalp. The roots are weakened and hair loss can occur. Excess oil makes your head a magnet for dirt, sometimes giving it the appearance of a string mop.

Scalp check-up – Part your hair at the crown and blot your scalp with a white tissue. If any residue shows, you have an oily scalp.

Magic hands

Nothing beats a great massage to stimulate the blood flow to the scalp, keep your hair in peak condition and relax you from your head down to your toes. Massage has not been scientifically proven to stimulate new hair growth however.

Begin by wetting your hair. Choose one of the natural ingredients listed below, depending on the condition of your scalp. Add a splash to some warm mineral water to make a solution. Drizzle the mixture through your hair massaging as you go.

Dry or tight scalp: Warm almond oil, sesame oil, or a light olive oil
Oily or greasy scalp: Astringents like witch hazel, lemon juice and cider vinegar
Normal scalp: Softening ingredients like jojoba and aloe

brushing up

Brushing is an essential part of hair maintenance. It keeps the scalp healthy by stimulating blood circulation, thereby feeding the follicles, and distributes your hair's natural oils.

However, too much brushing when hair is wet and vulnerable to breakage, can add stress. The best type of brush is one with a wooden handle and natural hair bristles. Avoid plastic bristles with pointy ends. If you want plastic, one that has rubber tipped bristles. Sharp metal bristles are definitely out. Another good choice is a large round brush to help straighten hair while drying it, give more body at the roots and control at the ends. The smaller the brush, the tighter the curl you get. The bigger the brush, the smoother the curl.

brushing basics

1 Start by raking your hair with your fingers using the back of your hand to get out snarls and tangles.

2 Comb the hair before brushing. Separate hair into small sections. Using a wide-tooth comb, work in a downward direction only.

3 Bend forward, allowing the hair to fall. Brush from the nape of the neck, over the head and down to the ends. Lift your head up, letting your hair fall normally. Brush from the underside of the hairline down to the ends. Lastly, brush the top layers into place with long, even strokes.

Caring for your brushes

Like your scalp, your brush suffers from oil
build-up and product overload.

- Remove hairs from in-between bristles after use.
- Wash your brush weekly using warm soapy water.
- Never immerse the brush fully in water,
  especially if it is wooden.
- Dry bristles thoroughly.

mane masterclass

When it comes to hair care, no matter the problem think seasonally. During the winter, there's no humidity in the air so hair flattens out as it loses moisture. Switch to lighter products and non-greasy formulas. For summer's high humidity, go with formulas that slick hair down and maintain shape and shine.

Problem: Frizzy

Try moisturizing shampoo and conditioner – avoid those containing protein, which can be drying. For curly hair, work anti-frizz gel through hair and blow-dry using a diffuser attachment. For straight hair, apply straightening cream, then divide hair into sections. Using a big round brush to hold tresses taut, blow-dry each section, aiming air down the hair shaft.

Fast fix: Finger dry roots to avoid overheating. Use a lightweight detangling spray. Rub finishing emulsion between your palms and smooth over any frizz.

Problem: Greasy

For greasy hair that needs frequent washing, avoid using shine-enhancing products, which can make greasy hair look stringy. Don't use creamy conditioners and waxes that stay on the hair shaft and put your oil production into overdrive. Don't over-brush. Use a dab of leave-in conditioner on the ends only.

Fast fix: Blot your scalp with oil-absorbing sheets intended for your face.

Problem: Lanky

Shampoo with a volumizing product, then apply a light conditioner to the ends. When your hair is 60 per cent dry, apply 5 to 10 spritzes of body-boosting spray to your roots. While blow-drying, lift sections of your hair with your fingers or a vent brush and aim heat at the roots.

Fast fix: Lift your hair at the roots and spritz with light, flexible-hold spray.

Problem: Fly-away

Static electricity is caused by friction between your comb and your hair, and between individual hairs. Don't comb too often. Conditioners coat the hair which provides insulation. Use the highest-level conditioner you can that doesn't weigh your hair down.

Fast fix: Lightly spray on leave-in conditioner or apply a few drops of silicone serum.

Problem: Hat head

This is a common sight in good weather when sunhats are worn to protect the hair from damaging UV rays.

Fast fix: Blow dry hair from roots to the end to add lift.

MANAGING IT

MANAGING IT

Half the battle is learning how to work with the head of hair you've been given. You may know best how your hair behaves, what it responds to and what pitfalls to avoid, but getting hair to look healthy, shiny and manageable can take a little knowledge, a lot of practice and some first-hand expert advice.

The best hair cuts are easy to style on your own and versatile so you can get a lot of looks out of them. It all starts at the salon. Sometimes it is hard to take a step back and figure out your hair options for yourself. A good stylist can look at you objectively and tell right away what will work for you and what won't.

No matter what kind of hair you have, every woman can have a bad hair day once in a while. There are days when you just can't be bothered or don't have the extra time it takes to devote to your style. Make a contingency plan. Your stylist can teach you the tricks you need to throw together a great look, no matter what mood you're in. Learning how to tie hair back, pile it up or twist it around can be a lifesaver when you're pressed for time or not in the mood. For special occasions, a quick blow dry by a professional is well worth the extra spend.

style ability

The key to managing your hair is getting to know how it behaves. Hair comes in three basic textures determined by the diameter or thickness of the strands.

Typical characteristics

Fine hair: 50 microns

• often hangs flat and lies close to the head • looks thin even if there is a lot of it • can look stringy and limp if worn longer than shoulder length • layers make thin hair appear even thinner • has a silkier feel than thicker hair • is easily curled and coloured • is often wavy, but rarely curly • colouring helps to add volume as it plumps up each strand • is ideal for highlights

Medium textured hair: 60–90 microns

• is the most common of all hair types • has a consistency somewhere in between silky and wiry • can be either straight, wavy or curly, with some variations • perming can give it the appearance of being thicker with more body

Coarse hair: 100+ microns

• is stronger and sturdier than fine or medium hair • is able to withstand processing better than fine or medium hair • often appears bushy or wiry in humid atmospheres • tends to look dull even after it is just washed • needs constant conditioning • tends to be dry on the top layers when it is curly • retains water easily when it is straight

In the thick of it

The thickness of your hair is related to the number of hairs on your head. Each strand can be as thin as 1/1,000 of an inch or as thick as 1/140 of an inch. Thick hair is always desirable, no matter what hair trends are in vogue, but can have it's styling woes too. For one thing, it's a lot harder to comb through.

The long and the short of it

The biggest problem with caring for long hair can be summed up in one little word: BREAKAGE. The longer the hair, the more susceptible it will be to fly-away strands, split ends and brittleness. Styling should start with gentle finger raking. Then brush the hair, smoothing down strands in between strokes.

Short hair can start to lose its shape in a very short time so may require more frequent trims than a longer hair style. Generally, the shorter the style, the more often you will need a reshaping.

Sleeping beauty

Something as mundane as the way you sleep can affect your hair's health. If you are a restless sleeper, you may be getting your hair caught between the pillows. Switch to a satin covered pillow so your hair can slide more easily when you move about. Putting long hair up with a soft covered wrap or scrunchy can also help keep it in place.

REALITY CHECK:

If you have long hair, a good way of gauging its thickness is to make a ponytail and place your thumb and forefinger around it. If the diameter is less than about 5/8 inch, your hair is thin. If the diameter is greater than 7/8 of an inch, your hair is considered to be thick.

hot stuff

Of the many styling tools that use heat, the blow-dryer is used most commonly. Curling tongs come in second. Whatever you use, be careful not to heat-damage your hair.

Nothing helps you achieve a fuller look than a blow-dryer in well trained hands – it is an indispensable tool. However, the heat produced by styling tools can make chemical changes in hair which in turn can cause discolouration and have a negative effect on the surface lipids and protein structure. Heat can literally boil out the water content in the hair shaft as it turns to steam, which severly damages the cortex. Over-exposure to heat will make any type of hair look and feel dry and lifeless.

The heat is on

Approach blow-dryers with caution, especially if your hair is not in good condition to begin with. Always hold a blow-dryer at least 6 inches from your scalp and vary the temperature settings, using high heat only for short spurts. Keep the blow-dryer moving, don't hold it on one spot for too long. The hair concentration nozzle that comes with most blow-dryers helps keep hot coils as far away from the scalp as possible. The best ones to use have a narrow plastic nozzle with a thin slit which direct heat on one

BEAUTY BYTE:

For more tips on caring for your hair, try

www.haircare.co.uk or www.clairol.com

area at a time without ruining the adjacent section that you just finished drying. Diffusers – the cone-shaped attachments that fit on the barrel of blow-dryers – are good for diffusing the airflow over a larger area and drying hair more slowly. These work well for curly hair to hold the curl. The most effective blow-dryer should have enough power to get the job done – from 1,200–2,000 watts. Beware of cheaper models that often use more heat than needed.

The same rules apply when using curling tongs. Go for a set with a cool tip designed to use easily with one hand. Some models have an automatic safety shut-off switch to control the temperature settings. You can bake a cake at 180°C, so imagine what your curling tongs are doing to your hair with their average temperature of 140°C. Blow-dryers are slightly cooler at 120°C whilst hot rollers usually work at 100°C.

If you've been on an all-out blow-drying or tonging mission lately, your hair may feel like damaged goods. Give it a rest and time to repair itself. Try using a specially designed absorbent hair towel that can dry hair in record time. Some conditioning and styling products are heat-activated to get treatment directly to where the potential for damage is greatest. They can slow down keratin breakage and stimulate the metabolism of the hair root. Air dry your hair naturally in the sun to switch off.

the drying game

Whenever you can, let your hair dry naturally in between blow-drying sessions but for those special occasions follow these steps for safe styling.

- Towel dry your hair and comb it through with your fingers.

- Begin drying with a blow-dryer, just aiming hot air at the roots.

- Bend forward and dry the bottom layers. If you have long hair, guide the hair up and over the head to add volume.

- Standing upright again, work with the back section, first using your hands, then blow-drying.

- Next do the sides, directing hot air towards the roots.

- For further volume, hold individual sections of the top layer straight up when drying.

- When your hair is nearly dry, finger comb through.

- Apply a low heat to the front section.

- For definition and control, use styling gel on the ends and shape with the hands. You may want to finish with a light hairspray, to hold your style.

life style

The environment can wreak havoc with your hair. Exposure to UV rays has the same effect on your hair as it has on your skin.

Environmental damage causes physical changes in hair, including the destruction of cuticle cells, roughening of the hair surface, loss of elastic strength and increased porosity. The porosity of the hair refers to its ability to absorb moisture. Such damage shows up more easily in lighter hair colours.

Hair enemies

The enemy	Hair protection
Salt water	Rinse or wash your hair after swimming in the sea.
Sun exposure	Wear a hat or scarf; use a spray with a sunscreen.
Steam heat	Use a humidifier at night; apply a conditioning treatment weekly.
Chlorinated pools	Wash hair immediately after swimming.
Extreme temperatures	Wear a hat to keep hair covered.
Wind	Keep hair pulled back; wear a cap.
Pollution	Use a spray with a sunscreen; use clarifying products.

Any harsh natural condition can have a negative effect on the quality and strength of your hair. When the hair is damaged, dirt and other particles can get lodged between the scales, which makes hair look dull. Grey hair is particularly susceptible to damage from the sun, which can give it a yellowish tint. Several sunscreens have been created especially for hair. These contain UV protection that filters out UV rays. The chemical names for these sunscreens are DDABT and Incroquat UV-283. They can be found in leave-in conditioners, detanglers and finishing sprays. They are most effective in products that are not rinsed out, and can be re-applied during the day as needed, or after swimming. If your hair is exposed to the sun a lot, it is a good idea to avoid using a blow-dryer. Sun and blow-drying present the worst possible combination for your hair.

BEAUTY BYTE:

For more information on high-tech hair care ingredients, visit www.uspto.gov/patft/index.html

Working hair

A day at the office can cause stress on your strands. As the day progresses, your hair may need a pick me up. The lack of moisture in recycled office air can strip hair and leave it looking dull and flat. Frizziness and static is not far behind. Heat from heating systems, fluorescent lighting and overhead bulbs contribute to dryness. When your work environment is warm or humid, you will start to sweat. Sweat contains salt which gets lodged in your hair and can cause dehydration. Perspiration from anxiety and running around can also be hard on the hair and flatten out your style before lunchtime.

frazzled follicles

Dry hair is a relative concept. Hair can react dramatically to the way you treat it. You may think your hair is dry because of insufficient moisture and oil content, but think again.

In fact, if your hair does not have a normal sheen or texture but is dry and brittle it may be the result of excessive washing, harsh detergents, heat processing or a dry or hostile environment. Friction is another culprit. Rough brushing or over-combing, even fabric pillows and pillowcases can cause friction on the hair which can be potentially damaging (see page 29).

One way to combat the coarse, brittle look and texture of dry hair is by using conditioners. If your hair is on the dry side, use a conditioner after every shampoo to achieve softness and shine. Bear in mind however, that even conditioners cannot really revitalize or fix severely damaged hair.

If your hair is constantly dry and intensive conditioning doesn't seem to help, see your doctor. Fragile hair that breaks easily may be a sign of more than just a problem of vanity. It may be caused by an underlying medical condition, such as metabolic diseases, hypothyroidism or poor nutrition.

Abnormally dry, lifeless hair may also be a result of the natural oil being stripped from the cuticle due to any of a number of causes. Hair tends to dry out during the winter in cold climates and can become dry after the use of steam heat, long periods of sun exposure or when a build-up of flakes clogs oil glands. Any tool that adds heat, like blow-dryers, curling tongs, straightening irons and electric rollers, can cause further damage to hair.

damage control

Naturally dry or heat-damaged hair needs extra tender loving care. The first step should always be prevention. Once the damage is done, it is harder to repair.

- **DO** apply a drop of shine-enhancing serum or cream to damp hair after washing.

- **DO** use a shine-enhancing spray if you have straight hair. Mist all over.

- **DO** allow your hair to dry naturally whenever possible or dry just the underside with a blow-dryer.

- **DO** use a cream conditioner on the ends of your hair twice a week. Cover hair with a towel and leave on for 20 minutes. Alternatively work a few drops of olive oil through once a week.

- **DO** use a humidifier in your home to replace any moisture lost from your hair.

hold it

Styling products can add shine and texture, as well as control flyaway hairs. The goal is to set your style once and maintain it for as long as possible throughout the day.

The worst mistake that women make is to use too many products at once, that have conflicting or overlapping missions. Determine your hair type and stick with just enough products to get the style you want and keep it, but no more. Each product will leave some ingredients on the hair that can weigh it down. Typically, a little bit goes a long way no matter what type of hair you have. Hair should always be soft, silky and irresistibly touchable.

Less is definitely more; the thicker or stickier the styling product feels, the less you need. The less you touch or handle your hair, the better it looks. The finer or thinner your hair, the less product you should use. Overcompensating via extra styling can lead to hair disaster – learn when to leave well enough alone.

Gels and mousses – These are basically interchangeable. They are both designed to hold, and add shine and texture. Gels come in lighter, user-friendly spray-on formulas for even distribution. They are generally worked through the entire head to give hair some shape, form and staying power. A light gel can help add body and volume to your hair but stay away from thick, gloopy gels that weigh hair down. For fine, thinning hair, look for gels that offer thickening, light or medium hold. Mousses are good because they are light and foamy and work well for finer curly hair, but they tend to be more drying.

Directions: These should be used on clean hair that is partially dry or just damp, rather than on dripping wet hair when they weigh strands down. Avoid applying before using curling tongs, since the heat may cause your hair to stick to the tongs if the gel or mousse melts down. Use a small dollop (the size of a one-pound-coin) squeezed into your palm, rub palms together to spread evenly and apply lightly. Use mostly your fingertips to scrunch waves and curls, and open palm to create a smoother, sleeker look. For longer hair, applying fixatives from midway down the hair will give a better hold. Comb through if needed to distribute evenly. Applying gels near the roots or brushing products through the hair will flatten out your curls.

Sprays – Styling sprays create your style, whereas holding sprays keep it in place. Stiff hairsprays are always a no-no. Avoid products labelled 'maximum hold' which can defeat the purpose of adding volume to hair by making it sticky. Sprays which contain alcohol tend to be more drying; ditto for aerosols. Non-aerosols often provide less hold, but give a more natural look and feel. If your hair is thin or limp, use a fine misting spray. Holding sprays may contain polymers that act as the fixative. The finer the mist, the smaller the droplets deposited. Sprays also keep humidity out, which keeps your style in shape.
Directions: Spray a small amount evenly over your style from a distance of about 30 cm. Don't spritz too close to the hair as this will cause build-up. You may want to reapply later in the day, so don't overuse.

Waxes and pomades – These should be reserved for thick, curly and coarse hair types and should never be used on fine or limp hair. Waxes are heavier than pomades and work well to create spiky styles or tame unruly ends. Pomades are applied to slick hair down and keep it frizz-free in humid weather.
Directions: Use only a dab rubbed on the palms and/or fingertips to distribute evenly through the hair. Use sparingly to avoid a greasy, flat look.

scissor hands

One of the simplest ways to keep hair in peak condition is with frequent trims. Whether long or short, hair should be trimmed on a regular basis, approximately every 6–8 weeks.

Waiting longer between cuts allows ends to go dull and become susceptible to breakage. There is no miracle product to repair split ends. However much you are tempted, ignore the gimmicks. The only way to get rid of ends is to cut them off. When growing out layers, make sure you have a reshape on a regular basis. As well as keeping your hair healthy, this maintains maximum fullness.

TOP TIP:
Don't skimp. One of the best beauty investments you can make is to get a great hairdresser.

Hair stylists are usually the first people to notice any problems such as hair loss. They have the advantage of being able to see the back of your head without the awkwardness of holding a hand mirror. It is worth taking the time to find a hairdresser you bond with and who will be honest if there is a problem.

Fringe elements

If you are trying to grow out layers or a fringe, you will need frequent visits to the salon to maintain a style. When your next hair appointment is still two weeks away, the boldest souls may be tempted to start clipping. Unless you're desperate, don't trim your hair yourself. Most professional hairstylists will allow you to pop in to have your fringe touched up in-between haircuts to keep your style in check.

If you have no option but to do a DIY job, follow these tips to get the job done right: use a straight comb with wide teeth, very sharp haircutting scissors (not the ones in your kitchen drawer) and gel to give you added control. Secure the rest of your hair leaving only the fringe hanging loose to avoid any nasty accidents. A soft, wispy fringe that sweeps along the eyebrows is the most flattering. It should frame your upper face and brow area. The endpoint should generally be your brow bone. A short, choppy fringe or one that is cut straight across can look more severe. Many women over 40 enjoy the fringe benefits of covering up forehead lines, wrinkles and creases. A well-tailored fringe can camouflage an ageing forehead or hairline that is too high. It can also save you a fortune in BOTOX® shots.

Tearing your hair out

Ponytails and tight plaits tug on hair and cause breakage. Always make ponytails using covered hair bands rather than the rubber ones you'll find in your desk drawer. Scrunchies, cloth-covered bands and ribbons are a good alternative to thin elastic bands. The wider the band, the less tension on the hair. Vary where you place your ponytails from day to day, especially those placed high on the head, and give your hair a day off regularly to limit the stress on your hair. Be especially careful when you remove bands, clips and barrettes from your hair because you can pull out hair that gets tangled in them. Choose hair ornaments that do not have sharp edges. Bungee elastics that have a hook at each end can be used to pull hair into a ponytail or bun without making knots, by wrapping them around your hair until it is tight enough and then just hooking the ends together.

the search for a stylist

Finding the right stylist is like dating – it's a long-term relationship and chemistry counts. Communication is also key. It may take time to get to know and understand each other.

- Ask for recommendations from friends. When you are out and about, if you see a woman with a hairstyle that you really like, ask her who she goes to.

- Go for a complementary consultation. Look around at the stylists and clients. Don't just put your head into someone's hands on a first visit.

- Get a list of prices for all the treatments offered to avoid a shock later. Choose a stylist you can afford to encourage more frequent visits.

- Tell your chosen stylist about your lifestyle, what you do for a living and how much time you have to devote to your hair.

- Communicate the type of look and length you're going for and if you wear glasses, take them with you.

- If you don't like the way the cut is turning out, stop the stylist immediately to discuss it.

- If you think a different stylist in the same salon might suit you better, you can switch, even though it may feel awkward.

- One bad haircut doesn't mean you should switch stylists if you have been happy in the past.

PROCESSING IT

PROCESSING IT

Natural materials like henna and indigo have been used to colour hair for the past 3,000 years. Technology has made great progress in producing safe hair dyes, so you no longer have to be stuck with the head of hair you were born with. At one time, covering grey represented the major market in hair dyes. Today, women no longer wait until they see their first grey hair to consider enhancing their own natural colour.

Instead of damaging follicles, colour is now considered beneficial to hair and the best method of adding volume and lift. The colouring process plumps up the hair cuticle, fattens each strand and adds texture and shine. Everyone's hair, except perhaps if it is in a severely damaged or weakened condition can benefit from adding one or more varieties of colour processing.

Your natural hair colour is determined by the type of melanin present. Eumelanins produce black or brown hair. Pheomelanins produce blondes or redheads. The colour, and I mean your 'natural' colour, also tells you something about the amount and type of hair. The more pigment in your hair, the darker its colour. As we age, pigment fades and the hair turns grey. When pigment is lost altogether, the hair becomes white. As if we didn't know already, blondes - with around 120,000 hairs compared to brunettes with an average of 100,000 hairs - not only have more fun, they also have more hair.

riding the waves

It's a well-known fact among women that we always want the hair we weren't born with. Don't fight with the hair nature gave you. Work with what you've got.

Don't waste time wishing your hair was stick straight when you have naturally curly locks, or longing for rolling, bouncing curls when your hair is perfectly waveless. If you try to go from curly to straight, or straight to corkscrews, it can be an uphill battle. If you do fancy a change, go for a less drastic one. Going from straight to soft waves or from curly to wavy should work.

The safest way to add curl is to use regular rollers and wind hair loosely around them. Curling tongs vary, making tight little ringlets or loose waves, depending on their diameter. Larger tongs work well to add body, volume and texture. Some have attachments that will straighten as well as crimp hair. Choose a model that is protected with a cloth surface, to cushion hair. Hot sticks – mouldable foam-like plastic tubes – are gentle on hair but not ideal for precision styling. Heated rollers can be used safely if they have fabric coverings to protect hair from heat damage. Velcro rollers are a universal favourite. Use them in dry hair for about 20 minutes, to reduce frizz and add body and control.

FOLLICLE FACT:

Curl varies according to ethnicity

● Asian, Chinese, Indian – the cortex is round, so the hair tends to be straight.

● African, Black – the cortex is flattened and curved, so the hair is more curly.

● White, Caucasian – slender, cylindrical with varying curves so the hair can range from straight to curly.

BEAUTY BYTE:

For tips on hair care for women of colour, visit
www.beautyandsoul.com

Relaxed attitude

To straighten out curls or kinks, a relaxer is applied all over the hair and combed through. The chemicals smooth the hair by softening the bonds inside, that give hair its curly shape. The treatment is then rinsed out thoroughly and a neutralizer is applied, to maintain the hair's new shape. Relaxed hair is particularly dry and delicate and needs continuous conditioning to keep it healthy and shiny. You can colour hair that has been straightened in this way. Use the relaxer first, then wait at least a week before colour treating it. Bear in mind the chemicals in the relaxer may lighten hair slightly.

DIY colour

Colouring your own hair is not for the weak at heart. Getting it right may look easy but it isn't always foolproof.

There are many good hair dyes suitable for home use, but getting it right may look easier than it really is. Hair dye can leave a mess in your bathroom sink, stains on your towels and on your hands if you don't use gloves. The safest place to start is with a gentle semi-permanent colour and follow the directions religiously. Always do a strand test to get the timing right. Many formulas are developed to stop working once the required amount of time has elapsed, to prevent disasters. If you have a particularly sensitive scalp, do a patch test the first time, to make sure you don't end up with a rash or irritation. Most off-the-shelf products on the market today are less harsh than in the past. Cream formulas are usually more buffered than liquids and the lower the pH, the gentler on your follicles.

> TOP TIP:
> Applying a moisturizer around your hairline and ears will help prevent the colour from staining your skin.

Temporary hair colouring products come in foam or gel formulas and can be shampooed in to last for about 4–6 shampoos. They are a good way to have fun, create interesting highlights, camouflage small amounts of grey or freshen up fading permanent or semi-permanent colours.

Bathroom blondes tend to look like they did it themselves. For a good result, you need to put some thought into choosing a colour. If it isn't quite right, you'll need an expensive salon visit to sort things out. If it's your first time, have a professional do your colour initially.

Green team

To avoid turning your gorgeous colour a vivid shade of green, stay out of chlorinated pools. Chlorine can react with the chemicals used to process hair, which can cause the colour to turn. It damages the structure of the hair and strips away natural oils. Wear a swimming cap and always rinse your hair immediately after swimming in a pool. Clarifying formulas can also help correct a greenish hue.

'Natural' blonde

You don't have to go lighter – the length and cut of your hair are what's really important – but virtually any woman who wants to try life as a blonde, now can. Even women with dark eyes, olive skin and dark brown hair can make the transition. If you're tempted to go golden, there has never been a better time. If you don't want to become a slave to the salon every 3–4 weeks, try highlights first. Flat or one-dimensional blondes like platinum require more maintenance. Lightening hair can also create a thicker appearance by matching the hair more closely to the scalp.

Great colour should look natural but even better. All it takes is time and money. An advertising slogan from the 1950s which asked 'Does she or doesn't she?' then referred to going blonde from a bottle. The results from hair dyes are so natural looking nowadays it's more likely to refer to BOTOX®.

shades of grey

Perhaps the most dramatic age-related change that every woman eventually experiences is greying hair. Most women start to see grey from their early 30s to middle 40s.

For the most part, going grey is genetically determined – you may notice a change in colour around the same age as your mother. As you age, everything gets lighter as pigment fades, including your hair which turns grey due to a lack of melanin pigment through decreased melanocyte function. This is irreversible. Blondes, redheads and light brunettes usually go grey, whereas those with darker brown and black hair are more likely to turn white.

Grey hair can take on a yellowish tinge from the effects of sun, wind and pollution. Colour-enhancing shampoos and conditioners can help cut brassy tints. Brightening shampoos prevent discolouration and add shine. Extra conditioning is needed for grey or white hair, which tends to be more coarse and dry. As the cortex goes, hair gets more wiry, dry and brittle which can make it harder to manage. Use deep conditioners, leave-in lotions and silicone-based anti-frizz gels for taming. Shine products add lustre to greys, which can look dull and flat.

Nothing ages a woman faster than grey hairs. Your choices are to keep the grey, cover it or let it gradually come in without taking over. To cover grey, hair can be dyed back to its original colour or slightly lighter. For partial coverage, semi-permanent colours can add a touch of silvery or slate tones. Permanent dyes conceal more grey. Lowlights can emphasize silver and grey by darkening selected strands of hair.

TOP TIP:

When dying grey hair, a softer, lighter shade in the same range as your original hair colour is often the most flattering choice. Bright or dark shades can look harsh and accentuate sallow skin tones. When changing your hair colour, don't forget your eyebrows. For darker hair, keep brows 1–2 shades lighter and for lighter colours or blondes, keep brows 1–2 shades darker.

LOSING IT

LOSING IT

Being follically challenged is not a laughing matter. Hair loss is a natural part of the ageing process, along with sagging necks, stained teeth and wrinkles. Lost hair is often dismissed as another casualty on the road to getting older. While it can be the bane of your existence, thinning hair doesn't have to be the end of the world. Most women under 50 assume that it is caused by external factors, while older women tend to attribute it to ageing and stress.

If you think you might be imagining a few extra hairs wedged between your bristles lately, you're not alone. Many women think thinning hair is a man's problem but hair loss is more common in women than you think. For every 5 men with hereditary hair loss, there are 3 women experiencing the same condition. It can begin as early as your 20s and is so common, that by the age of 35, almost 40 per cent of women demonstrate some of the signs. By the age of 50, half of all women will experience some degree of hair thinning.

Women often miss the early signs of thinning, thinking that their hair is simply becoming finer. Putting off seeking medical attention to find out why your hair is thinning can make the difference between effective treatment and having to live with it.

ages and stages

The life of the hair is similar to the life of the skin. In your 20s, you love your hair then, somewhere in your fourth decade, your first grey hair arrives. At first, there are only a few and they are easy to pluck out, but with each passing decade, the number of grey hairs increases.

20s Hair grows fastest from the age of 16–24 • Strands turn darker • Oil glands work overtime

30s First stray grey hairs appear • Hair starts to get finer • Hair needs extra protection from damage

40s Grey hairs are coming in fast and furious • There are now too many grey strays to pluck • Due to a reduction in oestrogen levels, hair thins and becomes drier and duller

50s The menopause and loss of oestrogen contribute to further hair loss • Your long hair days are over • Hormone fluctuations can make you lose hair from your head and grow it on your face

60s Your hair has turned from grey to white • The oil glands have slowed down, making hair drier • Your hair continues to thin out

TOP TIP:

Mature women have hair that is thinner and sparser so shorter, blunter cuts tend to work best.

follicle physiology

Hair grows about ¹/₂ inch per month, but as we age our rate of hair growth slows along with cell turnover and metabolism.

Your hair is thickest at age 20 and you have from 90,000 to 180,000 hairs on your head. Each little strand has its own growth cycle. The average hair fall is approximately 100–125 strands per day. These hairs are replaced. When lost hairs are not regrown or when more than 125 hairs are shed daily, it is likely that there is a true hair loss problem.

Hair is 97 per cent protein. The remaining 3 per cent is made up of amino acids, minerals and assorted trace elements. A hair follicle is a cavity of cells that forms a bulb around the base of the hair in the scalp. The root of a strand of hair is embedded about ¹/₈ to ¹/₅ inch into the intricate maze of nerves and sebaceous glands in the scalp. It is fed by a network of blood vessels that provide the nutrients necessary for growth. Although hair has no feeling, it is not dead. It receives a blood supply but has no nerve connections of its own to provide sensation.

Somebody who is in the early stages of hair loss will find that once it has started, it continues in a natural progression. An increasing number of follicles will shrink. A miniaturized follicle has a progressively shorter

BEAUTY BYTE:

Learn more about the structure of your hair at www.keratin.com

Follicle phases

The healthy follicle repeatedly goes through 3 phases:

1 Telogen – Resting Phase

At any given time, 10–15 per cent of your follicles are in a resting phase. This lasts for between 2 and 6 months.

2 Catagen – Transitional Phase

After resting, a follicle sheds its hair and grows a new one. The length of this phase is typically 3 weeks.

3 Anagen – Growing Phase

The follicle grows a hair for 2–6 years. At the end of this time the follicle will enter the resting phase once more.

growing phase that results in shorter hair and more frequent shedding. The new hairs that are grown become smaller and thinner. Eventually the follicle dies, producing no hair at all.

FOLLICLE FACT:
Your hair grows slower in cold weather because circulation is more sluggish.

reasons for hair loss

Hair is alive; it grows, it rests, it breaks, it dies and it falls out. It needs special care and not all hair is the same. Proper hair hygiene is essential to promote a lifetime of healthy hair.

The best way to keep it from falling out prematurely is to thicken what you've got from the inside out and to maintain its strength and condition. Finding hairs in your sink is not necessarily a sign of thinning hair; it could be going through the usual process or it could indicate a temporary hair loss condition. If you are not on your way to balding, your hair will grow back just as strong. If you are however, your hair will grow back finer and will not grow as long as it used to before falling out again.

Countdown

Each morning, collect the hairs from your pillow, bed linen, shower drain, hairbrush, comb and clothing. Count the hairs and put them into an envelope, marking the day and the number of hairs on the envelope. Use a new envelope every day for 2 weeks. Keeping a hair count will give you a basis for determining whether your attempts to regrow hair or slow down the rate of loss, are working.

TOP TIP:
To camouflage a thinning area, experiment with turbans and scarves and accessories such as flowers, fabric covered clips and wide bands.

A dozen reasons why your hair is falling out

1. **Genetics** – you are likely to suffer the same hair loss as your mother
2. **Emotional and physical stress** – can cause temporary thinning
3. **Rapid weight loss, crash diets and poor nutrition** – wreak havoc on hair
4. **Health condition and long illness** – temporary until condition ends
5. **Environmental damage** – exposure to UV radiation causes hair loss
6. **Hormonal flux** – the major culprit of hair thinning
7. **Poor circulation or iron deficiency** – cause weakness in hair
8. **Infection or high fever** – can cause temporary losses
9. **Medication** – certain drugs are deadly for your scalp
10. **Chemicals** – healthy hair is easily damaged by them
11. **Harsh brushing** – overdoing it can cause breakages and hair loss
12. **Aggressive scalp massage** – don't have too much of a good thing

splitting hairs

When it comes to ponytails, size counts. If yours seems to be getting skinnier, you may be starting on the road to thinning. A great hairpiece, hat collection or scarf-tying tricks can work wonders, but there are ways to hold on to your hairs.

If the cause is largely genetic, topical medications may be a good place to start. More serious hair loss conditions may require a transplantation, to help you to keep up appearances. If you are suffering from excessive hair loss, before you set off on a search for wigs or hair transplants, your first step should be a consultation with a dermatologist to determine the root of the cause. The best time to begin treatment is in the early stages when you first begin to display signs of hair loss, not when you're totally bald. As with any medical condition, hair loss responds better to treatment if it is caught early.

Rooting out the cause

Female hair loss can be difficult to diagnose as different conditions have a similar appearance at first glance. Every doctor should take a detailed medical history and possibly perform diagnostic tests to determine the cause of your hair loss. There are certain questions your doctor should ask and you should be prepared to give him honest answers. There are some health conditions that can go undetected, which contribute to hair loss. For example, an underactive or overactive thyroid gland and iron deficiency can make you shed too much hair. You may not know you have either condition and hair loss may be the first sign.

Diagnostic testing

After carefully examining the scalp and hair, further tests may be needed to zero in on the causes. These tests are used as a screening mechanism to determine general health, as well as specific abnormalities that may contribute to hair thinning.

Diagnostic tests

Thyroid function tests – checking the Thyroid Stimulating Hormone to rule out thyroid abnormalities

Blood tests – studies to measure blood lipids, Complete Blood Count (CBC)

Hormone levels – DHEAS, Testosterone, Androstenedione, Prolactin, Follicular Stimulating Hormone, Leutinizing Hormone, to identify hormonal conditions

Iron deficiencies – Serum Iron, Serum Ferritin, Total Iron Binding capacity (TIBC), to rule out anaemia

Venereal Disease Research Laboratory Test (VDRL) – a test to rule out syphilis, a disease that can cause patchy hair loss

Once the underlying cause is identified – if one can be pinpointed – it should be treated. For example, if you have a thyroid condition, thyroid-replacement hormones may be prescribed. Women with heavy menstrual periods can develop an iron deficiency due to blood loss. If you have low serum iron, iron pills may be recommended.

getting the shaft

There are many reasons why your hair may be falling out;
for starters, genetics, stress, diet, hormones and chemicals.
Some of these are entirely out of your control.

The most common cause of thinning hair is
heredity and can be passed down from either
your mother's or your father's side of the
family. The more bald people there are in your
family, the greater your chances of losing your
hair. Contrary to common myth, it does not skip a
generation. The propensity is passed down from any
and all of your relatives. About half the people who have one balding
parent of either sex will inherit the dominant gene for baldness.

FOLLICLE FACT:
Balding is predominant
among Caucasians and
more common in those
with fine hair.

Hormonal flux

Periods of hormonal change are a common cause of female hair loss.
Many women do not realize that they can lose their hair after pregnancy,
following discontinuation of birth control pills or during the menopause. The
changes that occur during pregnancy usually slow down the shedding
process, which is why some women's hair becomes so nice and thick.
Within a few months of childbirth though, the hair that did not get shed
during pregnancy sometimes seems to fall out all at once. Hair loss may
not show up for 3 months following the hormonal change and it may take
another 3 months for the normal growth pattern to be fully resumed.

Tress stress

Surgery, severe illness and emotional stress can also have a negative impact on your hair. The body can simply shut down the production of hair during periods of stress since it is not necessary for survival and instead devotes its energies towards repairing vital body structures. In many cases there is a 3-month delay between the onset of stress and the first signs of hair loss. Furthermore, there may be another 3-month delay before the return of noticeable hair regrowth. Thus, the total hair loss and regrowth cycle can last 6 months or possibly longer when caused by physical or emotional stress. Although they will not cause balding on their own, physical and emotional stress can adversely affect the quality and strength of the hair. Stress does not cause permanent hair loss.

Cosmetic surgery

One of the most common complaints women have after a facelift is that they are losing their hair, specifically along the sides of the head. Hair loss can also come as an unwanted surprise after a brow lift. The cause is often the tension of the suture or stitches placed in the hair follicles. Newer, more modified facelifts can be designed to avoid making any incisions in the hairline for this reason. The good news is that it's usually a temporary condition and regrowth occurs within the first 3–4 months. If you are already experiencing thinning hair and are contemplating a lift, talk to your surgeon to determine your risk level. Some plastic surgeons may recommend you to take a course of Minoxidil (see page 82) before and after surgery as a precaution. Take it twice daily for a period of 4 months for best results.

scalp conditions

The state of your hair follicles can be the clearest indicator of your general health and overall wellbeing. The condition of your scalp can also provide clues to your hair health.

Hair today, gone tomorrow

A healthy scalp provides a strong foundation for a gorgeous, shiny head of hair. If hair loss is accompanied by an itchy scalp or skin irritation, it could be a sign of underlying medical causes. Doctors may do a Scalp Biopsy, taking a piece of scalp to be sent for pathological examination, to determine any further abnormalities. For example, Ringworm, caused by a fungus infection, shows up with patches of scaling, redness, swelling, and broken hair.

Without an accompanying scalp condition, hair loss can still be an indication of internal causes like illness, vitamin and mineral deficiencies, a low blood count, anaemia, hormonal changes or the body's response to surgery or anaesthesia. It can be a symptom of a many health-related factors, including thyroid abnormalities and autoimmune disease, as well as exposure to certain chemicals such as lithium salts, lead, mercury, selenium, arsenic, thallium and borates. It can also result from taking some antibiotics, beta-blockers and antidepressants and certain drugs for cholesterol and arthritis.

Drugs linked to hair loss

Amphetamines – diet pills

Antibiotics

Anti-coagulants – Coumarin, Heparin

Anti-convulsants (for epilepsy) – trimethadione (Tridione)

Anti-depressants – Tricyclics, amphetamines

Beta blockers (for high blood pressure) – atenolol (Tenormin), metoprolo (Lopressor), nadolol (Corgard), propranolol (Inderal), timolol (Blocadren)

Chemotherapy agents

Cholesterol drugs – clofibrate (Atromid-S), gemfibrozil (Looped)

Contraceptives

Gout drugs – Allopurinol (Loporin, Zyloprim)

Male hormones (anabolic steroids)

Non Steroidal Anti-inflammatories (NSAIDs)

Parkinsons Disease drugs – levodopa (Doper, Larodopa)

Radiation Agents (used in radiotherapy)

Salicylates (aspirin derivatives)

Thyroid drugs – carbimazole, Iodine, thiocyanate, thiouracil

Ulcer drugs – Cimetidine (Tagamet), ranitidine (Mantic), Cimetidine (Pepped)

Vitamin A derivatives – Tretinoin

diet details

Abnormal hair texture, sheen and colour may be a symptom of certain stages of malnutrition. Hair loss can be caused by fad dieting, eating disorders or just not eating well.

Crash diets by their very nature don't meet the minimum Required Daily Allowance (RDA) levels. Temporary hair loss may occur as a result of the stress and shock that crash dieting can put on your internal systems. Protein or iron deficiencies may affect your hair count. From a dermatologist's standpoint, supplemental vitamin pills cannot prevent the hair loss that is associated with losing weight rapidly. Many over-the-counter diet supplements are high in Vitamin A, which can often make hair loss worse.

The simplest advice is to get sufficient vitamins and minerals in your diet by eating enough protein – meat, poultry and soya – and foods containing essential fatty acids, especially olive oil and fish. Drinking 3 glasses of skimmed milk per day also helps. If you have difficulty getting enough essential nutrients into your diet, eat as healthily as you can and take a multi-vitamin supplement.

Treatments and supplements made from herbs and roots have been cited as cures for hair loss, but data is sketchy and there are no guidelines regarding correct dosage or side effects. Many studies have been done in countries where testing parameters are lax. None are scientifically proven to actually stop hair loss or encourage regrowth. Ask your doctor before taking anything.

BEAUTY BYTE:

To learn more about the causes of hair loss in women, log on to www.womenshairinstitute.com

girl stuff

The most common type of hair loss seen in women is androgenetic alopecia, also known as female pattern alopecia or baldness. This involves thinning of the hair, predominantly over the top and sides of the head.

It is diagnosed in approximately one third of all women who experience hair loss and is most commonly seen after menopause, although it may begin as early as puberty. Women lose hair differently to men and it is usually less severe. Unlike men who tend to lose hair in one concentrated area, women are prone to an overall thinning that starts at the top and gradually spreads. After a while, the scalp will become see through. The frontal hairline usually keeps its original shape. Women may also experience the typical male hair loss pattern (receding hairline, bald spot on top). A small percentage of men suffer from overall thinning, more typical of female pattern loss.

> **TOP TIP:**
> If your hair is white, grey or blonde, there will be less of a contrast between hair and scalp.

The medical term for hereditary hair thinning is androgenetic alopecia. It affects men and women of all races, skin and hair types. The possible causes are heredity, hormones and age. It can lead to progressive miniaturization of hair follicles and shortening of the hair's growing cycle. The active growth phase becomes shorter and the hair follicles smaller, so the follicles gradually produce finer and thinner hairs. Eventually, there is no growth at all.

BEAUTY BYTE:

For more info about alopecia areata, visit

www.naaf.org

Alopecia Areata is the second most common form of hair loss. In most cases it is temporary, thus regrowth is possible, particularly in adults. Although the cause is not clearly known, it is widely considered to be an autoimmune condition. This means that the body produces antibodies that fight against substances normally found in the body, such as hair follicles. Sufferers will find that follicles will stop producing hair abruptly. Heredity plays a role in approximately 20 per cent of Alopecia Areata cases, but nearly 90 per cent will only experience occasional episodes. Its mildest form can show up as small, circular patches where less than 50 per cent of scalp hair is lost; the more severe form involves more than half of all scalp hair. It can respond to a range of medical treatments that include topical steroids, cortisone injections, PUVA light therapy, oral antibiotics, Minoxidil and topical Anthralin which is used to treat Psoriasis.

The two other basic types of Alopecia are Alopecia Totalis, which is the complete loss of scalp hair, and Alopecia Universalis, which involves the total loss of all body hair. Both of these conditions are very difficult to treat.

Other types of temporary hair loss

Anagen effluvium – generally due to internally administered medications – such as chemotherapy agents – that poison the growing hair follicle.

Telogen effluvium – occurs when more than the usual number of hair follicles enter the resting stage. When the causes are dealt with, such as stopping certain medications, normal hair growth should return.

questionnaire

questionnaire

A medical examination uncovers whether hair loss is due to any underlying disease or condition. If there is none and hair loss pattern is typical, no further tests are needed.

HAIR LOSS PATTERN:

- How long have you been suffering from hair loss and at what age did it start?

- Are you experiencing increased shedding or thinning?

- Is your hair coming out by the roots or is it breaking along the shaft?

- Have you suffered from irritation of the scalp?

- Has your hair always been slightly dry? Is it always like this or does it fluctuate?

MEDICAL HISTORY:

- List any medications you are taking or have taken in the past.

- Have you ever taken Birth Control Pills and, if so, for how long?

- At what age did you begin menstruation?

- Describe your periods / pregnancies / menopause.

- After your last pregnancy, did your hair grow back finer or lighter?

Have your immediate family members, such as parents or brothers and sisters experienced hair thinning?

Have your extended family members, such as grandparents or aunts and uncles experienced hair thinning?

Have you ever had any major illnesses or severe infections?

Have you had flu or a high temperature recently?

Is there any other significant family medical history?

List any other symptoms that you have.

Have you ever seen an endocrinologist?

HAIR CARE REGIME:

What shampoo(s) do you use regularly?

What conditioners do you use regularly?

How often do you wash your hair?

How do you normally style your hair?

How often do you use a blow-dryer, curling tongs or rollers?

Do you or did you ever colour, perm or chemically process your hair?

EATING HABITS:

Do you follow a particular diet / have any special dietary requirements?

Do you take any vitamins or supplements?

RESTORING IT

RESTORING IT

Having a hair transplant may never occur to many women, since it is usually thought of as something reserved for men. Gone are the days when a hair transplant made a scalp look like a field of newly planted corn. New technology and improved surgical techniques are transforming hair transplant methods. Large grafting procedures that gave transplants their plug-like appearance are a thing of the past. The new methods allow for more hairs in each skin graft, to be placed between existing hairs, promoting greater hair density.

The first hair transplants were performed in Japan in the 1940s. In the 1950s, New York Dermatologist Norman Orentreich MD pioneered hair transplantation by using grafts taken from the back and transplanted to the front of the head. The 1970s saw the introduction of the first transplants (see pages 86-87). In the 1980s, scalp reductions became popular. This involved reducing the area of bald scalp by surgical excision and pulling the hair-bearing skin together to make the area of baldness smaller. Mini- and micrografts were also introduced, along with mega-sessions (see pages 88-89). Follicular Unit Hair Transplants (FUHT) gained acceptance in the 1990s and remain popular due to their natural appearance.

self care

The chance of suffering from thinning hair is twice as high for women with fine hair, as for those who start out with a thick mane. There are ways to conceal fine or thinning patches.

The great pretenders

Colouring the scalp with over-the-counter products can reduce the contrast between the colour of the hair and the scalp. Hair loss concealers come in spray, powder and pencil form and are applied to the hair and scalp, either to make the hair appear thicker or darken the scalp. Some can achieve both. These concealers are for areas of thinning hair, not slick bald areas. The disadvantage of such products is that they do not do anything to prevent you from losing hair in the long run and are only a temporary solution. There is a risk that the concealer will come off or run in the rain or in severe humidity.

Hope in a soap

There is a whole category of shampoos, conditioners, serums and gels that promote a variety of theories about how to prevent hair loss. Some systems claim their products induce hair growth by dosing the scalp with vitamins, marine extracts, copper complexes and other nutrients. Other products are said to contain deep-cleaning agents that open up clogged hair follicles, allowing these tiny sacs to sprout new hair shafts. Some of these products may be effective as scalp conditioners and make hair appear healthier, but they tend to do very little, if anything, to actually reverse hair loss. Buyer beware.

hair restorers

What you see in the mirror over a long period of time is the best monitor of early signs of thinning. You may notice areas of hair that no longer need cutting or where the hairs are getting shorter and finer.

Specialists

Trichologists administer non-medical treatment for scalp and hair problems. The term simply means 'hair specialist' and carries no specific training or licencing. Typically, a qualified trichologist will have completed an educational programme that covers the anatomy and physiology of the skin and hair. During an initial consultation, the trichologist will analyze both hair and scalp under a microscope to determine the problem and the best way to treat it.

Caveat Emptor: Before you sign on the dotted line, be wary of hair restoration clinics that ask you to pay in advance for extensive programmes without any written guarantee of results. Expect to pay a consultation fee and if treatment is recommended, ask to pay at the time of the treatment. Clinics will sometimes offer a free consultation to induce you to come in.

Medical doctors, specifically dermatologists, should be consulted over more severe hair loss with numerous internal causes which may respond to prescription medications.

mane attraction

Hair additions are used both for cosmetic and medical reasons. Extensions provide a fast track route to longer hair, while hair weaves are just one way to cover up thin or thinning hair.

Modern forms of hair additions have made great strides in simulating a natural, fuller appearance. The main reasons women want extensions are either to add length or extra body and volume. Hair weaves, extensions, hairpieces, non-surgical hair replacements and partial hair prostheses are commonly used. If you want long hair instantly, the fastest way to get it is with extensions. A high-quality, well-fitted system can be virtually undetectable. Anyone who has had a badly done hair transplant may find the best way to camouflage it is to wear a hair addition. If your hair is thinning to the point that emergency measures are needed, a hairpiece can give you a good match to your own hair colour.

Instead of opting for total hair replacement in the form of wigs, women with thinning hair often choose the more comfortable and natural looking partial hair additions or integrated units. However, the downside is that the pressure on existing strands may eventually lead to bald spots. Hair weaving and other types of attachments like temporary clips attached too tightly to fine hair, can place prolonged tension that can cause permanent hair loss at the anchor site. The latest model extensions are designed to minimize the potential for damage.

There are two basic choices for hairpieces:

Synthetic fibre – more durable than human hair; new materials like Prolin don't become discoloured and the ends won't split.

Human hair – colour fades faster than the lesser quality synthetic; it has a more natural feel and is typically more expensive.

Partial hair additions are attached using a variety of techniques. Either the existing hair or the scalp can be used as the anchor site.

Hair to hair – such techniques attach extensions or pieces to the existing hair, to provide more security for the active lifestyle. They are all dependent on the existing hair and must therefore be reattached or tightened as it grows. Hair units that are attached with clips, weaves or tape can be very secure as long as they are attached properly.

Stick it to me – adhesives such as double-sided tapes and the new improved waterproof liquids can fit securely. Stickies are also used to help you keep a hairpiece on comfortably. If you have sensitive skin, have a patch test done in advance to make sure you are not allergic to the adhesive. Hair units that are physically bonded to your skin can be worn while swimming or on the most blustery day.

Vacuum bases – tunnel grafts are small skin grafts taken from a donor site and formed into a small loop, which is used to fasten removable inserts, permanently attached to a hair addition.

Regular cleansing of the scalp and hair is vital when wearing a hair addition for extended periods. Hair additions should be inspected regularly for changes in colour or texture. A hair addition can be expected to last about 18 months before it begins to lose its natural appearance and may need to be replaced.

hair growth stimulators

Certain drugs for hair loss are considered 'off label', or not officially approved, although recommended for other conditions. Many gain approval once enough clinical data is collected.

Minoxidil

Topical Minoxidil is currently the only medication approved by the US Food and Drug Administration for female pattern hair loss. It was approved for men in 1988 and for women in 1991. In the US, topical Minoxidil is marketed under the brand name Rogaine®; in the UK, Europe and New Zealand it is marketed as Regaine®. It is available over the counter at chemists and hair salons in 3 formulations; Regular, Extra Strength for Men, For Women. A generic version of 5 per cent topical Minoxidil is available under the brand name Headway.

This anti-balding drug is a topical ointment applied directly to the scalp. It increases blood flow to the scalp, which has been associated with increased hair growth. More potent formulas can be obtained through a doctor since it can cause irritation and itchiness in higher doses. The downside is that it has to be used forever to maintain hair growth. If you stop, the normal hair loss process will start again and you will lose your newly regrown hair in 3–4 months. Minoxidil® is not a cure for baldness but it can slow down the hair loss process and retain the hair you have. If you get regrowth it's an added bonus, but there is no guarantee.

How to use it: You will be prescribed Minoxidil 2%, Regaine® or Minoxidil 5% or Rogaine® Extra Strength. Apply twice daily. Results show after 4 months.

Finasteride

Propecia® is a tablet taken once a day. Approved by the US Food and Drug Administration in 1997 for male pattern hair loss, this drug is given orally, and with continued use, has been shown to help preserve existing hair. This pill blocks the conversion of testosterone (the male hormone) into a hormone called dihydrotestosterone (DHT), which on its own converts normal hair follicles to non-hair follicles, thus triggering hair loss. It may also be combined with Minoxidil. Finasteride is not generally recommended for women of childbearing age as it can cause abnormalities in the growth and development of a foetus.

There are certain drugs used to treat hair loss that are considered 'off label', which means that they are not officially approved for hair loss although they may be approved for other conditions. The fact that they are 'off label' indicates that their effectiveness varies widely and they are not appropriate for everyone. Many drugs start out being prescribed for 'off label' uses and eventually do get approved for the condition they are being used to treat when doctors and drug companies have collected enough clinical data.

Dutasteride

A drug called Dutasteride is the hottest treatment for hair loss sufferers, but so far only for men. It works by blocking two enzymes that convert testosterone into a nasty, hair-killing hormone called dihydrotestosterone (DHT). DHT is a key player in hair loss because hair follicles in balding individuals are more sensitive to inhibition by DHT. Finasteride blocks only one of the enzymes responsible for making DHT. DHT also causes the prostate to grow, which leads to problems for some men.

hormonal help

The best hope for women who don't want to undergo surgery lies in the area of hormone treatments. Oestrogens compete wtih androgens for control over the body, so raising the ratio of female to male hormones, often helps hair loss.

Some doctors prescribe a topical .025 per cent oestrogen solution daily or every other day. Progesterones have been used for hair loss in both men and women, given orally and by injection. Some doctors recommend progesterone precombined with Minoxidil. Taking oestrogen-dominant oral contraceptives (estradiols) may also help. Post-menopausal women can also take oral oestrogen as a treatment.

Anti-androgens

Anti-androgens interfere with the actions of androgen hormones. Spironolactone, a steroid and powerful anti-androgen, is often prescribed for hair loss since it is not absorbed throughout the body. Other anti-androgens used for hair loss include Flutamide, Casodex and Dexamethazone. The star performer, considered to be the most effective drug for treating hair loss in women, is Cyproterone Acetate (Androcur). Androcur or Cyrprostat contains 50mg of Cyproterone Acetate, making it the most powerful anti-androgen available. It is used for women who have too much androgen production and/or are particularly sensitive to the activity of androgens in their bodies. It is also used to treat acne, overactive oil glands and hirsutism (hair growth). In most countries,

TOP TIP:

Many doctors recommend monthly breast examinations when using topical oestrogen formulations due to the potential increased risk of cancerous tissue and fibroid growth.

Androcur can only be prescribed by a medical doctor. Cyproterone Acetate is available in the UK by specialist prescription. A form of this drug is available as a solution that can be mixed with Minoxidil and applied directly to the scalp. Potential side effects include liver failure and your doctor will require you to have regular liver function tests.

Expert Advice: Most experts agree that making dietary changes and using topical solutions offer the best combination treatment available, other than surgery.

fuzz buzz

Although there is an abundance of so called remedies for baldness in a bottle, the only true way to restore your hairline is to get help from a specialist.

Hair transplantation, formerly one of the most tedious and labour-intensive cosmetic surgery procedures, is now a simple day surgery done under local anaesthetic. The best type of procedure depends on the extent and pattern of hair loss. Often a combination of techniques will be needed. The ideal candidate for hair transplants is a woman who has either female pattern or male pattern baldness and enough hair on the back of the head to redistribute to where it is thinning. Female pattern baldness is progressive; the results you get today may not stay that way, so your surgeon has to plan your hairline and the density of transplanted hair for the long term.

Women are considered more challenging to treat for hair loss than men. As in most things, our expectations are higher. In a man, if he sees he has a little more on top and maybe looks a few years younger, he's usually satisfied. Women want thick, glossy hair all the time. Hair transplants can actually be simpler for women because they're able to hide them better. A woman can easily wear a scarf and because women's hair is generally longer, it's harder to see the incision. When new hair begins to grow, the effect on a woman's scalp is subtler. People may notice that your hair looks better but they won't be quite sure why. Something else to be aware of is that transplanting hairs next to existing hairs, can bring on traumatic shock, which causes existing hairs to shed. This can lead you to actually look worse after a procedure than before. The shock loss is usually temporary, but since the existing hairs may also be damaged by pattern loss, it is possible they won't grow back. If the transplant is done carefully so as not to disturb the existing hairs, it won't induce shock loss.

Transplants

Hair transplants can be likened to planting cuttings. The technique moves your own hair follicles from the back or side of the head and transplants them to the thinning or balding areas where they will regrow naturally. Done well, it can look very natural. After all, it's your own naturally growing hair. Small donor strips of hair-bearing scalp are removed from the back and sides of the head, which is an area of the densest hair for even the baldest heads. The area that grafts are taken from is called the 'donor site'. The beauty of the methods used today is that only ONE fine white scar in the back of the scalp is necessary. The surgeon can keep using the same hidden scar over and over for any transplant procedures that may be needed in the future. The strips of scalp are divided into grafts for placement in the balding areas. The hair-bearing grafts are carefully inserted into small holes or slits that are made in the balding scalp. The grafts can also be inserted between existing hairs to increase the density and thicken the area. Strategic planning and precise placement of grafts is essential to give the illusion of more hair.

REALITY CHECK:
Approximately one third of women with thinning hair are candidates for hair transplants.

mini- & micrografts

Mini- and micrografts are the most commonly performed hair restoration procedures for women, and they remain the treatment of choice.

The characteristics of your hair and scalp – including colour, texture, skin-to-scalp contrast, degree of curl, hair density, estimated future hair loss and how much donor hair you have – determine whether you are a good candidate for a graft. Over the last decade, the basic size of hair grafts has got smaller and finer. Micrografts as small as single hairs are commonly placed behind the hairline to provide a gradually increasing density. They are ideal to fill in the hairline region, a common problem area for women. Most surgeons use a combination of varying size grafts for the most natural looking results.

Micrograft – 1–2 hairs into needle holes

Small slit grafts – 3–4 hairs into a slit recipient site

Large slit grafts – 5–7 hairs into a slit recipient site

Small minigraft – 3–4 hairs into a small recipient site

Large minigraft – 5–8 hairs into a small round recipient site

A typical session takes 2–3 hours and it is now possible to have about 400–500 grafts of skin – containing 2–4 hairs each – redistributed from the back of the head to the front and top in one session. Initially the donor hair falls out within a few weeks or months, but

BEAUTY BYTES:

For more about hair restoration, log on to www.hair-transplants.net and www.ahlc.org

regrows about 3 months later. Within 4–6 months, you can see a huge difference and it continues to grow for as long as the hair would have done had it been left in the site from which it was removed. Despite improvements, transplants are labour intensive and require the skill of a surgeon along with a team of 3–5 assistants. Mega-sessions can deliver 3,000–4,000 grafts, taking 10–12 hours and involve several technicians. The amount of density that you can achieve depends on the number of grafts placed per session. Most women only require 1 or 2 treatment sessions for a good correction.

Lasers

The first laser hair transplant using a Carbon Dioxide laser, was performed in 1992. The holes or slits needed to reposition hair follicles can be made with the aid of Erbium:YAG or Carbon Dioxide laser technology. The laser creates very small punctures of a consistent depth and width, which in some cases can speed up the length of time the procedure takes. It causes less bleeding and incurs a shorter healing time than was previously necessary.

Future shock

Recombinant DNA Gene Therapy is the most likely prospect as a cure for baldness. Researchers have pinpointed the first human gene linked to baldness, which may provide key information on how hair grows. Through gene therapy, it may be possible to give you back the gene that codes you for a particular deficiency. Creams that contain the gene may eventually be developed, meaning it can be transferred via the body into the bloodstream. Alternatively, topical creams could be applied directly to the hair follicle. Scientists are currently working on hair cloning – a tissue-engineering technique that uses a single hair follicle to create thousands more which can then be inserted into a bald area of the scalp. The technology exists and doctors are working on refining the technique for the future.

choosing a surgeon

choosing a surgeon

Since hair restoration procedures rely on the skill and artistry of your doctor, you should see at least three doctors before going forward with surgical treatments.

There is a wide range in the quality of hair replacement surgery, which can run from looking really obvious to virtually undetectable. Through the use of variable-sized hair grafts along with improved instrumentation, experienced hair restoration surgeons can create a natural hair appearance by lowering a receding hairline and filling in thinning areas at the temples and crown with absolute precision.

Find out about a surgeon's qualifications. Typically, hair restoration surgery is performed by dermatologists and plastic surgeons, although general surgeons and GPs often perform these procedures too. Make sure your surgeon has extensive experience and training and does a lot of hair restoration procedures on a consistent, ongoing basis. Practise makes perfect.

BEAUTY BYTE:

To find a qualified doctor for hair restoration, check out www.asds-net.org, www.hairtransplants.com, www.ishrs.org and www.surgery.org

What to ask

- What training do you have, especially in new techniques? How many procedures of this type have you performed?

- What are the risks involved with the procedure? Find out how often they occur and how they will be handled if they do.

- What is your policy on surgical revisions? Find out about any costs for which you may be responsible if you are not happy with the end result and require a revision.

- What is the expected recovery time? Discuss postoperative restrictions on activity, what dressings will be used and when you can resume work.

- Since hair restoration is often done in stages, find out exactly how many sessions you will need, how they will be scheduled and what costs are involved with each.

- Ask to see photographs of other hair restoration procedures that the specialist has done.

- Ask to meet a patient who the surgeon has recently finished working with. Seeing the results firsthand is a good indicator of what you can expect to achieve.

- Will I be in pain after surgery and need someone to take me home?

- What will happen to the result if more hair loss occurs? Will it be necessary to have a second hair transplant in the future if the position of the hairline changes?

SUMMING IT UP

SUMMING IT UP

The appearance of your hair is central to how you feel about yourself and your overall self-confidence. Getting it right makes a world of difference to your look and sets the stage for your wardrobe, makeup and self-image. The key is to realize your hair's true potential and for that you need to turn to the experts. Nothing makes more of a difference to a woman's looks than a great cut and breathtaking colour. It is a lot more than just a fashion statement – it defines your total look and can be the thing that people will remember most about you. When it comes to great hair, if you've got it, flaunt it. If you don't, then learn how to fake it.

Just like your skin, hair needs consistent care and maintenance to do you proud. To keep hair in peak condition think protection. The goal is to make the most of what you've got and hold on to as many hairs as possible for as long as you can. Inevitably, as you age your hair will thin. How early and how much is partly predetermined for you. If you catch it early, there are medications as well as treatments that can help you. Remember that you are not alone. If you take thorough care of your hair to avoid unnecessary damage, your hair can be a real asset. As soon as you notice thinning, start with the basic treatments that are discussed in this book and work your way up, if needed, in order of progression.

First of all, see a dermatologist to determine the cause of your hair loss. Start applying any topical medications prescribed. Look into having hair extensions or shop around for a hair piece. You may be happy to stop at adding hair extensions, or you may be so troubled by hair thinning that you decide to have transplants. Treating hair loss medically requires a much smaller initial investment than having surgery done, but it can be less effective. Most experts agree that making dietary changes and using topical solutions offer the best combination of treatments available next to surgery.

Looking towards the future, the good news is that we can anticipate numerous advances both in the field of hair care products and colouring processes, as well as in the scientific arena regarding hair loss and regrowth.

index

acknowledgments

Special thanks to my gorgeous girl Eden Claire for giving me a reason to write. My great appreciation goes to Alison Cathie and Jane O'Shea for having a vision, and to Lisa Pendreigh and Katie Ginn for making it work.

I also wish to thank the many doctors, surgeons and experts who kindly gave their time and shared their knowledge with me to help with my research. Walter Unger, MD; Robin Unger, MD; Joel Kassimir, MD; Laurence Kirwan, MD; Nicholas Lowe, MD; Alan Matarasso, MD; Seth Matarasso, MD; Ronald Savin, MD; Zoe Draelos, MD; Laurie Polis, MD; Michael Roy; Elsa Serra at Stella; Ken O'Rourke; Jo Hansford.

For more information on getting gorgeous hair visit Wendy Lewis's website at www.wlbeauty.com or email your hair care queries to wlbeauty@aol.com.